THE
Guitar
Tablature Library

VOLUME TWO
Classical Collection II

Adelita	*Francisco Tárrega*	10
Air on a G String	*J. S. Bach*	8
Clair de Lune	*Claude Debussy*	25
Etude on a Theme by Mozart	*Ferdinando Carulli*	17
Four Short Performance Pieces	*Ferdinando Carulli*	
Number 1		30
Number 2		36
Number 3		39
Number 4		42
Lagrima	*Francisco Tárrega*	12
Liebesträume	*Franz Liszt*	21
Romanza	*Anonymous*	3
Romanza	*Matteo Carcassi*	13
Saltarello	*Vincenzo Galilei*	5
Songs My Mother Taught Me	*Antonin Dvorák*	23

Arranged by Christopher Sotnick

©1995 International Music Publications Limited
Southend Road, Woodford Green
Essex IG8 8HN, England

Tablature

Tablature is a system of notation using six lines in place of the five normally found in a musical staff. Each line represents a string of the guitar. Tablature enables players who have difficulty reading normal musical notation at a proficient speed, to see the finger positions immediately.

The fret positions to be played are numbered on the appropriate strings, and the timing is taken from the normal musical staff which is above the tablature staff. Various other playing instructions are found in tablature and are explained below.

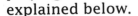
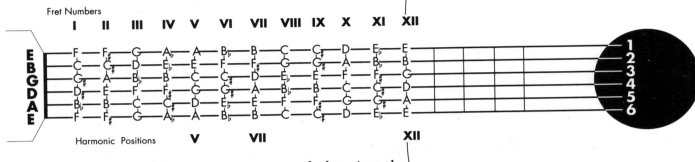

Barrés are indicated by a roman numeral showing the fret position thus: **II ----¬** This shows a Barré or single finger placed across the second fret. If the lower strings are to be played open, the a half barré will be indicated thus: ½ **II ----¬** .

Indicated below is a simple way to tune the guitar, assuming the low E string is at, or close to, its correct pitch.

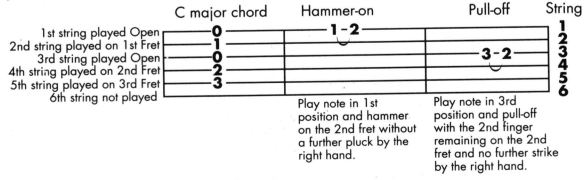

The above staff shows that if you finger the 6th string on the 5th fret you will produce an A, which is the tuning for the 5th string. Positions are marked above for the tuning of the other strings.

Chords are indicated as in normal musical notation with the notes in a vertical line, and a wavy line next to these notes indicates a broken chord (♩).

The above staff shows:

	C major chord	Hammer-on	Pull-off	String
1st string played Open	0	1-2		1
2nd string played on 1st Fret	1			2
3rd string played Open	0		3-2	3
4th string played on 2nd Fret	2			4
5th string played on 3rd Fret	3			5
6th string not played				6

Play note in 1st position and hammer on the 2nd fret without a further pluck by the right hand.

Play note in 3rd position and pull-off with the 2nd finger remaining on the 2nd fret and no further strike by the right hand.

Chord symbols are shown as an indication of the finger positions wherever it is helpful to the player. To avoid confusion, only easily recognisable chords have been inserted.

Romanza

Anonymous (19th Century)

©1995 International Music Publications Limited, Southend Road, Woodford Green, Essex IG8 8HN

Salterello

Set 6th string to D

Vincenzo Galilei

Air on a G String

J.S.Bach

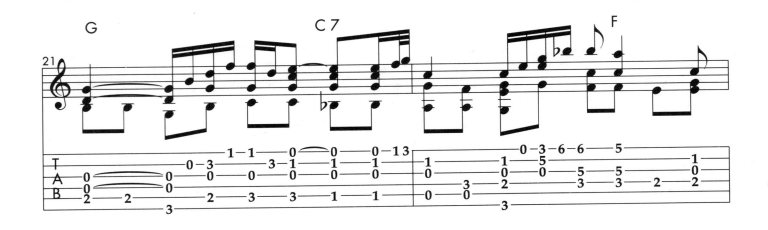

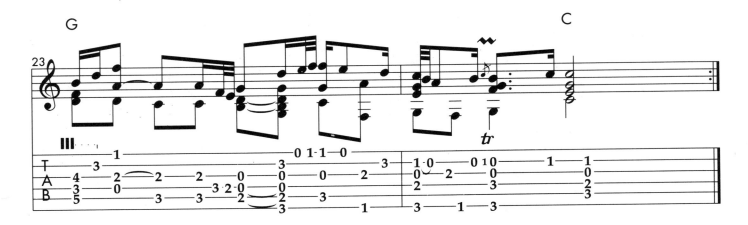

Adelita

Francisco Tárrega

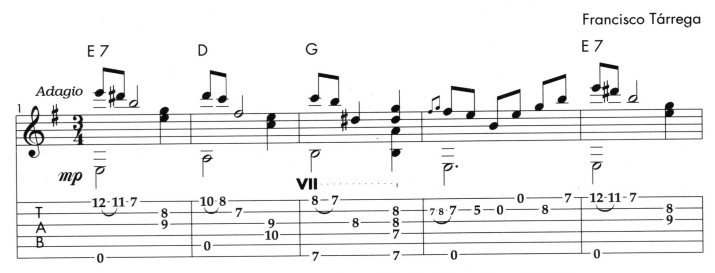

Lagrima

Francisco Tárrega

Romanza

Matteo Carcassi

14

Etude on a Theme by Mozart

Ferdinando Carulli

Liebesträume

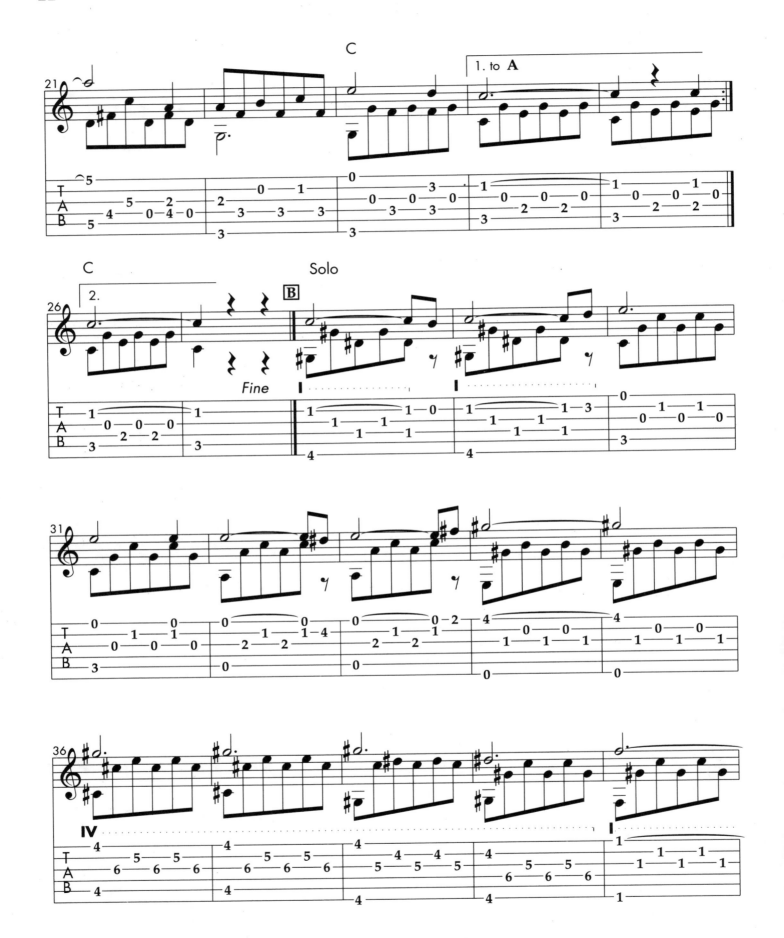

Songs My Mother Taught Me

Andante con moto

Antonin Dvořák

Clair de Lune

Andante très expressif

Solo guitar in E

Claude Debussy

Tempo rubato

merendo jus a fin

Four Short Performance Pieces
No 1.

Ferdinando Carulli

32

Nº 2.

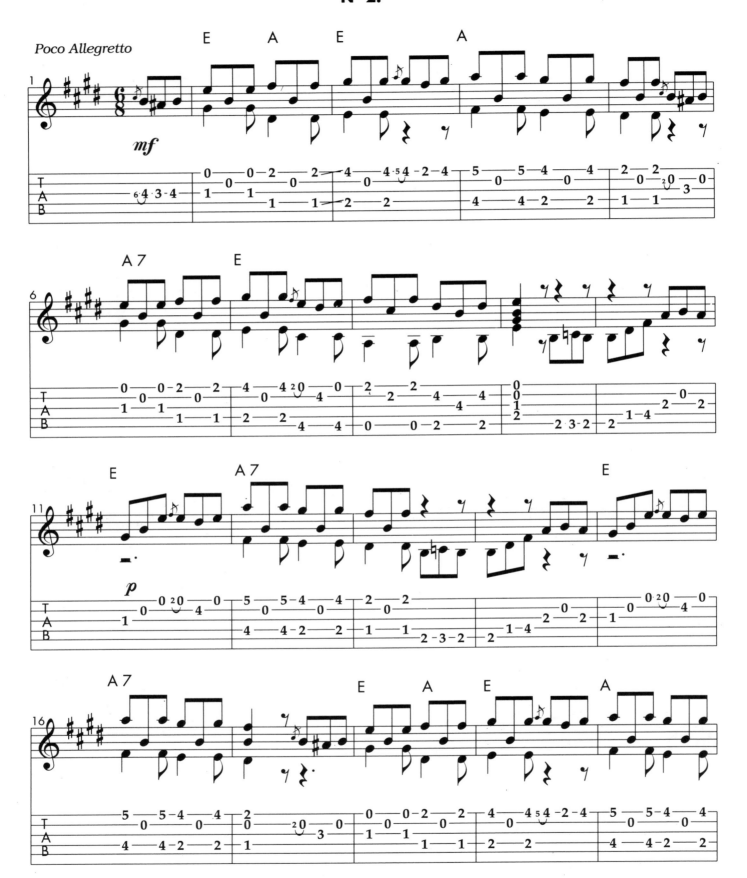

Nº 3.

Nº 4.

Andante con moto Solo Guitar in Key of C

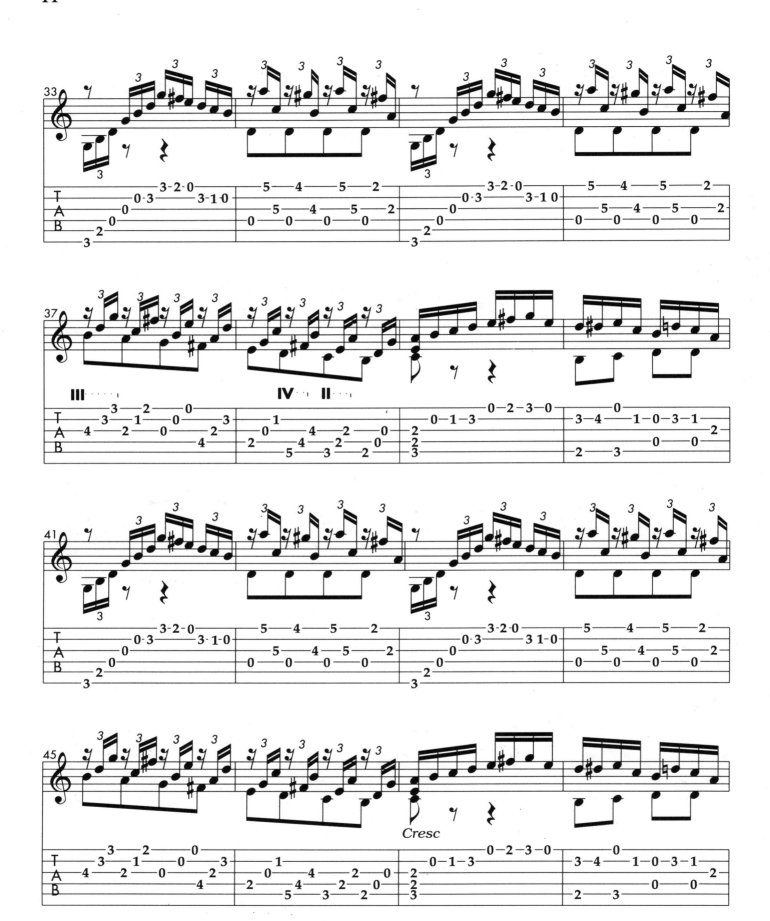

46

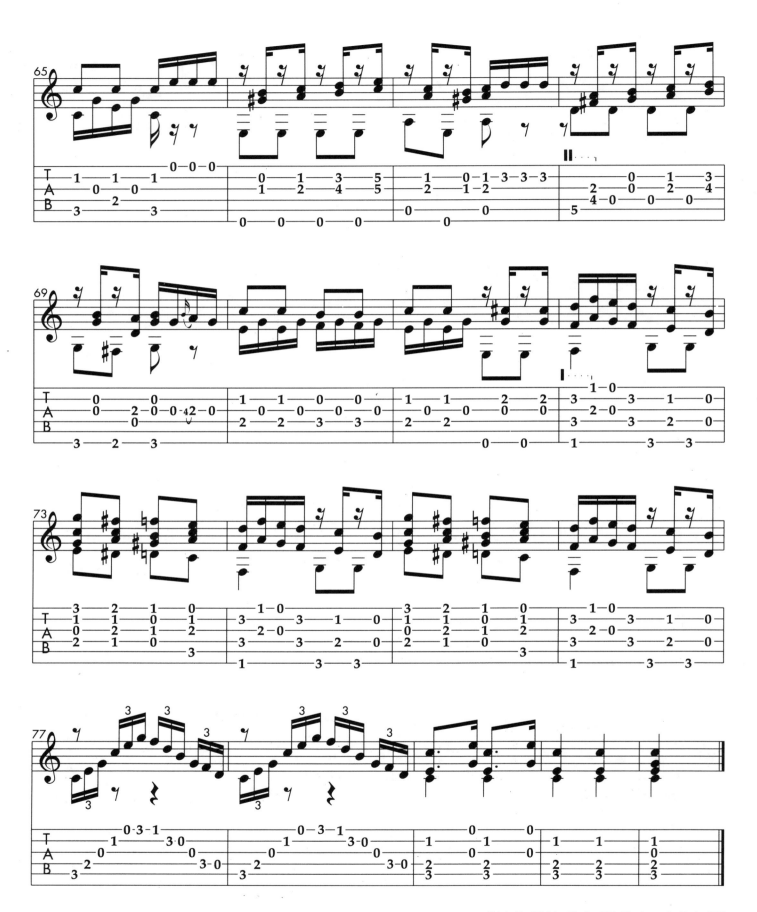

Printed by Watkiss Studios Ltd., Biggleswade, Beds. 2/95